CONTENTS

Find the Power Discs!

Ten tiny Rapunzel's Kingdom Power Discs have been hidden throughout this annual. Write the page numbers down here when you find them.

MEET THE HEROES

Welcome to a world of infinite possibilities and endless fun! Disney Infinity is packed with laughs, thrills and even a few scares. Meet some of your adventure guides . . .

> SOMETIMES I EVEN SCARE MYSELF!

SULLEY Got it!

Play Set: Monsters University.
Likes: Pulling stunts on his bike.
Dislikes: Those Fear Tech jokers.
Hangs around with: Mike.

Big, hairy and super-scary (when he wants to be), Sulley would rather be setting up traps for unsuspecting monsters than sitting in boring old lectures.

PURPLE SPOTS

MASSIVE PAWS

HEROIC CHIN

FISTS READY FOR POUNDING

> ALL RIGHT! WHO NEEDS SAVING?

MR. INCREDIBLE Got it!

Play Set: The Incredibles.
Likes: Slamming Omnidroids into scrap metal.
Dislikes: Super villains escaping.
Hangs around with: The Incredibles (who else?)

The greatest superhero in the world, Mr. Incredible has muscles on his muscles. No enemy can stand against his Super Ground Pound but don't let that amazing physique fool you – Mr. Incredible has brains as well as brawn.

LIGHTNING MCQUEEN [ ] Got it!

Play Set: Cars.
Likes: Putting the pedal to the metal.
Dislikes: Having to take a pit stop.
Hangs around with: Mater.

Lightning McQueen is ready to roar into action day or night. The racing champ does everything at top speed, whether that's pulling off awesome stunts or towing his fellow motors out of trouble.

I'M READY TO ROLL!

GO-FASTER FLAMES

LIGHTYEAR TYRES

MYSTERIOUS MASK

JUSTICE WILL BE SERVED!

SIX SHOOTER

THE LONE RANGER   Got it!

Play Set: The Lone Ranger.
Likes: Riding in at the last minute to save the day.
Dislikes: Crooks and outlaws.
Hangs around with: Tonto.

Who is that Masked Man? The Lone Ranger never gives up, charging into danger on his faithful steed, Silver. He's the fastest gun in the Toy Box.

JAUNTY HAT

CAPTAIN JACK SPARROW [ ] Got it!

Play Set: Pirates of the Caribbean.
Likes: Treasure.
Dislikes: Being told what to do.
Hangs around with: Barbossa.

Avast, ye landlubbers. He may be a bit of a rogue, but Jack's certainly a charmer, sailing the seven seas and getting himself in hot water wherever he swaggers.

TRUSTY CUTLASS

YOU CAN ALWAYS COUNT ON CAPTAIN JACK SPARROW!

JESSIE Got it!

Play Set: Toy Story in Space.
Likes: Riding Bullseye the horse.
Dislikes: Standing still for too long.
Hangs around with: Woody.

Jessie is the most excitable, rootin' tootin'-est cowgirl around. She can throw a mean Pixar Ball, too!

> SOMEONE CALL FOR A YODELLIN' COWGIRL?

ALWAYS READY TO SADDLE UP AND RIDE 'EM OUT. YEE-HAW!

MAGIC FINGERS

SORCERER'S HAT

SORCERER'S APPRENTICE MICKEY Got it!

Likes: His shiny red jalopy.
Dislikes: Nothing. He sees the good in everything!
Hangs out with: Anyone he can!

Sorcerer's Apprentice Mickey is everyone's pal and always looks on the bright side of life, whatever crazy situations he finds himself in. Just watch out if he's driving that old red jalopy. Oh boy!

> SAY, ARE YA' READY TO HAVE SOME FUN?

SUPER SKILLET

RAPUNZEL Got it!

Likes: Collecting lanterns.
Dislikes: Being told what to do.
Hangs out with: Maximus the horse.

This blondie is a bit of a dreamer, but sure knows how to let her hair down. She loves exploring, but is no pushover, especially with her trusty frying pan in hand!

> OH MY GOSH! THIS IS INCREDIBLE!

LONG HAIR

ANNA

Likes: Climbing.

Dislikes: Being alone.

Hangs out with: Her sister, Elsa.

Used to frozen conditions, Princess Anna is a girl with a warm heart. Courageous and loyal, she lets nothing get in her way – not even icy mountains, thanks to her handy climbing hook!

> I'M JUST YOUR RUN-OF-THE-MILL, NON-MAGICAL PRINCESS!

STRONG ROPE

WARM CLOTHES

SKULL FACE

STYLISH THREADS

> BOO!

JACK SKELLINGTON

Likes: Pranks.

Dislikes: Being serious.

Hangs around with: Anyone he can trick – or treat.

Funny-bones Jack will have you screaming with laughter. Nobody scares like the Pumpkin King (don't tell Sulley), and his flaming jack-o-lanterns are a real blast.

PHINEAS

Likes: Having fun.

Dislikes: Being bored!

Hangs around with: Agent P.

Here's a kid with more imagination than he knows what to do with. This madcap inventor never passes up the chance of going on an adventure, especially when he's armed with his baseball shooter. Three strikes and you're out!

> I THINK WE CAN OFFICIALLY CALL THIS THE BEST DAY EVER!

BIG SMILE

EVEN BIGGER EYES!

WORD UP!

Can you find all of these Disney Infinity stars hiding in the grid?

```
N X R T P M E X W E M S X A Y O E A B G E Z H L T
P O H A H T C M P R Y Q I K E W S Q W N L E H W U
R B T E P J V O E C E R A T L V E D D A B E L S A
O U A G F U L V P S O C R A L Q D K J M I U H D D
T A W F N L N E J L O C K R O H T M I A D V S O D
Q E Z K E I A Z G A V C F I H L J A M M E H A L V
V D L N R Z L G E D N E H S T Q D T V N R J D W R
W Z A O Z E N L R L E N H S C R Z E U V C A F S P
X V W U I G M E B B U A R A T A R C S N C I Y H
R D B C R V U C A K Z T M K P R L L H W I K O J I
S E N O J Y V A D B S O G W E Q L V P X S S C V N
Y K N F B V D Y F Q J K V N K X A J G H R P S Z E
D S Y D O O W H E Q D Q C C I F V U G L M A E Y A
E H L Q T A H H D Q A L W A K N H F O D A R C H S
M R I N C R E D I B L E T C J K T N W C R R N Q M
O T H E W R C E Y X P O N P U K E H W M T O A D Y
P O S S E L H T U R N O V N O R A B G K O W R V V
S Y N D R O M E H T Y X A E A K V T J I T S F H H
Q J P X M E U O O Y X O I N T V C P U Y L F J H T
R J K P Z F A U V H K S G W W T U X R I Q K R Q F
M C M O Z R I Q X Z S E W W J T R M L A Y W R S U
N P T M D L W V E R Z B F W I T J C S N M O O P
J Q K E Z N F S J I D X K G M X R X I X H D M Q B
N S R M L D Y Z M N J Z X L L L R Q N O O V Y Y Q
Y E L L U S K A D U G E C F P A G E N T P C N W K
```

AGENT P
ANNA
BUZZ
DASH
DAVY JONES
ELSA
FRANCESCO

HOLLEY
JACK SKELLINGTON
JACK SPARROW
JESSIE
LIGHTNING
LONE RANGER
MATER
MIKE

MR. INCREDIBLE
MRS. INCREDIBLE
PHINEAS
RANDY
RAPUNZEL
SULLEY
SYNDROME

TONTO
VANELLOPE
VIOLET
WOODY
WRECK-IT RALPH

Three mysterious villains have sneaked into the wordsearch. Can you find them too?

1.
2.
3.

SKETCH SULLEY

And you thought Sulley was quick on the draw with his paintball shooter! Grab a pencil and copy MU's star scarer square-by-square into the grid below . . .

READY TO PLAY?

Explore the Disney Infinity Play Sets!

TOY STORY IN SPACE

Calling all Space Rangers! Everyone's favourite aliens are in trouble. Help Buzz build a safe new world for the extra-excited extra-terrestrials. What's that? You're worried about fighting Emperor Zurg? Then the Star Command Combat Simulator will prep you for battle just in case the real tin-pot tyrant turns up!

TOP TOYS TICK LIST

- [ ] Bullseye
- [ ] Buzz Lightyear's Jetpack
- [ ] Goo Valley Transporters
- [ ] Star Command Boost Pack
- [ ] Medicine Ball

MONSTERS UNIVERSITY

It's Fear-It Week and pranksters are out in force. Can you keep Monsters University safe from Fear Tech raiders, while making a laughing stock of those FT jokers? The honour of MU is at stake, scarers!

TOP TOYS TICK LIST

- [ ] Beastly Bike
- [ ] Bat-Winged Pest Bush
- [ ] Fear Tech's Sludge Balloon
- [ ] Cracklin' Backpack
- [ ] Slithering Cycle

THE INCREDIBLES

Phew! The Incredibles have rounded up a gang of sinister super villains. Hurrah! Let's hope Syndrome doesn't break out his fiendish friends. Wait, he has? That means no one is safe. Metroville needs heroes and it needs them now!

TOP TOYS TICK LIST

- [ ] Mr. Incredible's Sports Car
- [ ] Glide Pack
- [ ] Hover Board
- [ ] The Incredicopter
- [ ] Zero Point Energy Gauntlet

PIRATES OF THE CARIBBEAN

Drink up, me hearties! We all know pirates love to pillage and plunder, rifle and loot but Captain Jack Sparrow is in deep water. Davy Jones has got his slippery tentacles on a treasure map that will give him mastery of the sea. Quick! Set sail and stop the soul collector before it's too late, savvy?

TOP TOYS TICK LIST

- [ ] Atlas Blade
- [ ] Voodoo Cannon
- [ ] Calypso's Rage
- [ ] Pirate Bomb
- [ ] Phase Shift

CARS

Luigi wants to bring the world's best racers to Radiator Springs. Will you test his new racetracks? Fillmore is ready to lend a wheel to help you take first place but you'll need to help him mix the ultimate engine fuel first.

TOP TOYS TICK LIST

- [ ] Tow Chain
- [ ] Missile Challenge
- [ ] Machine Gun Challenge
- [ ] Impact Mine Challenge
- [ ] Monster Truck Tires

THE LONE RANGER

The Cavendish Gang is causing trouble for the good people of Colby. They need a masked adventurer or a silent scout to run those crooks out of town and get the railroad back on track. Can you save the day, kemosabe?

TOP TOYS TICK LIST

- [ ] Silver
- [ ] TNT Pack
- [ ] Silent Warrior
- [ ] Elephant
- [ ] Thundering Stallion

YOUR PERFECT PLAY SET

IF YOU COULD CREATE A PLAY SET FROM ANY DISNEY FILM OR CARTOON WHAT WOULD IT BE? WRITE IT HERE:

....

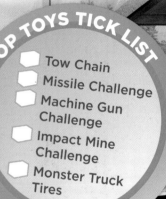

JOIN THE NSA

Hello, darlings! Have you got what it takes to join the National Supers Agency? Take Edna Mode's quiz and find out!

1. A policeman is trapped on top of a flaming building. What do you do?

A. Leave him where he is. You put him there in the first place. ☐
B. Call out for someone to help. ☐
C. Rescue him immediately, putting out the fire in the process. All in a day's work. ☐

2. Syndrome has been spotted creeping around downtown. What do you do?

A. Rush out and get his autograph! You're his number one fan! ☐
B. Hide beneath your bed until he goes away. ☐
C. Track down that dastardly villain and throw him out of town. ☐

3. Omnidroids are attacking the Town Hall. What do you do?

A. Join in! Town Hall will be destroyed. Mwa-ha-haaa! ☐
B. Rush and tell a policeman. ☐
C. Fly in and rip those Omnidroids to pieces. Pow! Smash! Etc! ☐

4. It's your day off, and Snoring Gloria has sent the entire city to sleep. What do you do?

A. Send her a 'congratulations on being a public menace' card. ☐
B. Snore. ☐
C. Round up her Sleep Pods. Heroes are always on duty! ☐

5. Where would you prefer to hang out?

A. Syndrome's evil lair. ☐
B. Metroville Zoo. ☐
C. The NSA Headquarters – you can use the spare time to train. ☐

6. A gigantic monster is attacking the bridge to the NSA Headquarters. What do you do?

A. Adopt it as a pet. Awww. It's so cute! ☐
B. Run screaming from the harbour. ☐
C. Pick it up by its tail, spin round and round and launch it into orbit. ☐

7. Do you look good in tights?

A. As long as they're diabolical electro-tights of doom! ☐
B. Not really. I prefer a comfy pair of socks. ☐
C. Yes, and capes, utility belts and those strange underpants you wear over your tights. ☐

8. An elephant has escaped from the zoo and somehow got stuck up a tree. What do you do?

A. Blast it with a monstrification ray to transform it into a MONSTROUS elephant stuck up a tree. And then blast the tree too, for good measure. ☐
B. Take a picture. The guys at home are never going to believe this. ☐
C. Lift the elephant down with one finger, transport it back to the zoo, mend its cage using your laser-vision and then plant a new tree just in case the old one got damaged. ☐

HOW DID YOU DO?

☐ If you answered mostly A:

YOU'RE NOT A SUITABLE CANDIDATE AT ALL. IN FACT, YOU MIGHT BE SYNDROME IN DISGUISE, YOU ROTTER.

☐ If you answered mostly B:

YOU'RE A LAW-ABIDING CITIZEN, BUT NOT REALLY NSA MATERIAL. SORRY.

☐ If you answered mostly C:

CONGRATULATIONS, DARLING. YOU'VE MADE THE GRADE. YOU MIGHT BE THE GREATEST SUPERHERO IN THE HISTORY OF THE WORLD. (DON'T TELL MR. INCREDIBLE!)

HEAD TO HEAD

Who's your favourite retro gamer – Wreck-It Ralph or Vanellope?
Rate the retro game buddies and discover who comes out on top.

	Wreck-It Ralph	Tick if Wreck-It Ralph should win:	Vanellope	Tick if Vanellope should win:
Most Likely to Say	'I'm gonna wreck it!'		'Aww, I'm adorable!'	
Height	Ralph looms over anyone he meets.		She's small and mighty.	
Hair	Spiky and thick (the hair, not Ralph).		Accessorized with a pink bow and lots of sweets.	
Style	No-nonsense lumberjack shirt and dungarees combo. No need for shoes with those stomping feet.		Cuter-than-cute peppermint hoodie and pleated skirt. Trainers for extra speed!	
Special Skills	Clobbering with those massive fists. A one-man demolition team.		Teleporting, Glitch-style, at top speed. Catch her if you can.	
Tools and Rides	Wreck-It Ralph's Cherry Bomb. Boom!		Vanellope's super-zippy Candy Cart. Vroom!	
ADD UP THOSE SCORES TO SEE WHO WINS!				

Why not put your other heroes in a head-to-head? Who would win out of Buzz and Woody? Or Elsa and Anna?

GET THE PARTY STARTED

Woody needs to get his Toy Box going with a bang. Which of these lines connects the confused cowboy's Power Switch to his Party Cannon?

WHAT COMES NEXT?

Can you fill in the gaps in the sequence that Hamm has been creating using his Creativi-Toys?

1

Kill Switch	Replayer	Timer	Kill Switch	Replayer	?

2

Target	Replayer	Bird's Eye Camera	Bird's Eye Camera	Replayer	?

START YOUR ENGINES

Luigi has opened a super-fast new track! Race your friends to see who can cross the finishing line first!

6 STUNT RAMP! SHOOT FORWARD THREE SPACES!

7

8 ROAR THROUGH A MOUNTAIN TUNNEL! FORWARD ONE SPACE!

5 OIL ON THE TRACK. SLIP BACK ONE SPACE!

18 SPIKES ON THE TRACK! MISS A GO WHILE THEY'RE CLEARED!

17

16

4

19

25

3 GET A TURBO BOOST! FORWARD ONE SPACE!

20 PULL OFF A TRIPLE-FLIP STUNT! WOO! FORWARD THREE SPACES!

24 STOP FOR A LITTLE TRACTOR TIPPING FUN! MISS A GO!

2

21

23

START

22 RAMONE GIVES YOU GO FASTER STRIPES! FORWARD ONE SPACE!

1 ON YOUR MARKS! GET SET! GO!

9

10 SUPRISE TELEPORTER! ZIP FORWARD TO 16!

11 CRASH INTO THE BARRIERS! BACK TWO SPACES!

12

15 MISS A JUMP! BACK ONE SPACE!

14

13 JUMP THROUGH THE RING OF FIRE! FORWARD ONE SPACE!

26 HIT A PINBALL FLIPPER! BACK THREE SPACES!

32 GET MONSTER WHEELS! FORWARD ONE SPACE!

33

34

27 FILL UP ON FILLMORE'S ULTIMATE ORGANIC FUEL! FORWARD TWO SPACES!

31

35 WOAH! SKID OFF THE TRACK! GO ALL THE WAY BACK TO 21!

28

30 TRACK CLOSED FOR REPAIRS! MISS TWO TURNS!

29

FINISH! YOU'RE THE WINNER!

WHICH MONSTER ARE YOU?

Think you're a top scarer? Discover which Monsters University student you're most like . . .

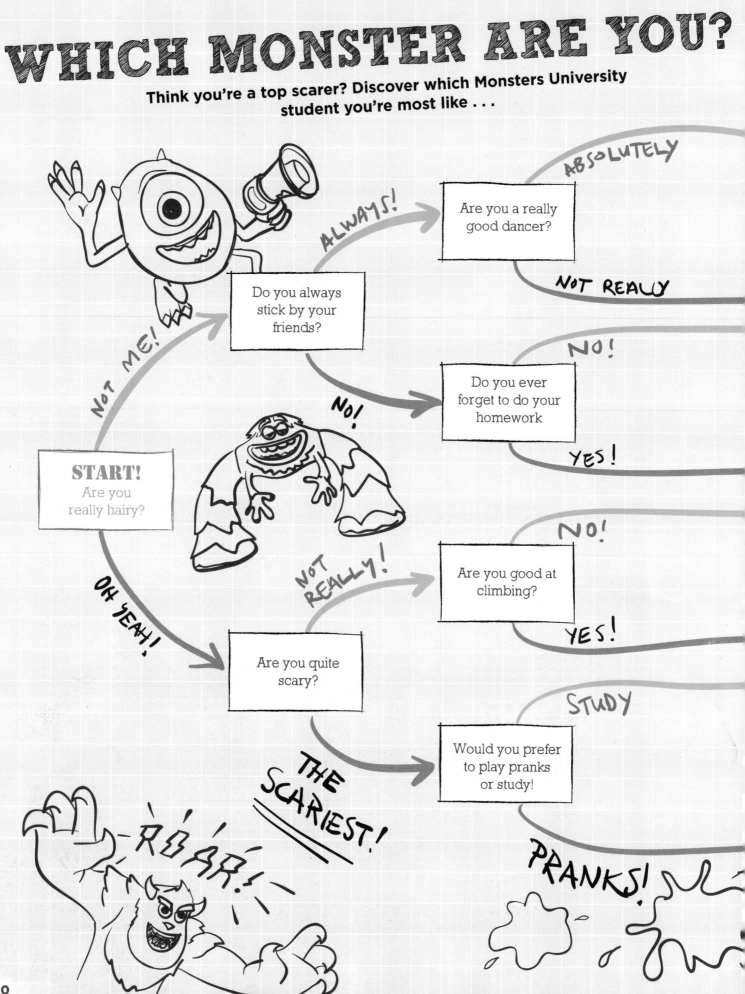

ABSOLUTELY

Are you a really good dancer?

NOT REALLY

ALWAYS!

Do you always stick by your friends?

NOT ME!

NO!

Do you ever forget to do your homework

YES!

START!
Are you really hairy?

NO!

NOT REALLY!

Are you good at climbing?

YES!

OH YEAH!

Are you quite scary?

STUDY

THE SCARIEST!

Would you prefer to play pranks or study!

ROAR!

PRANKS!

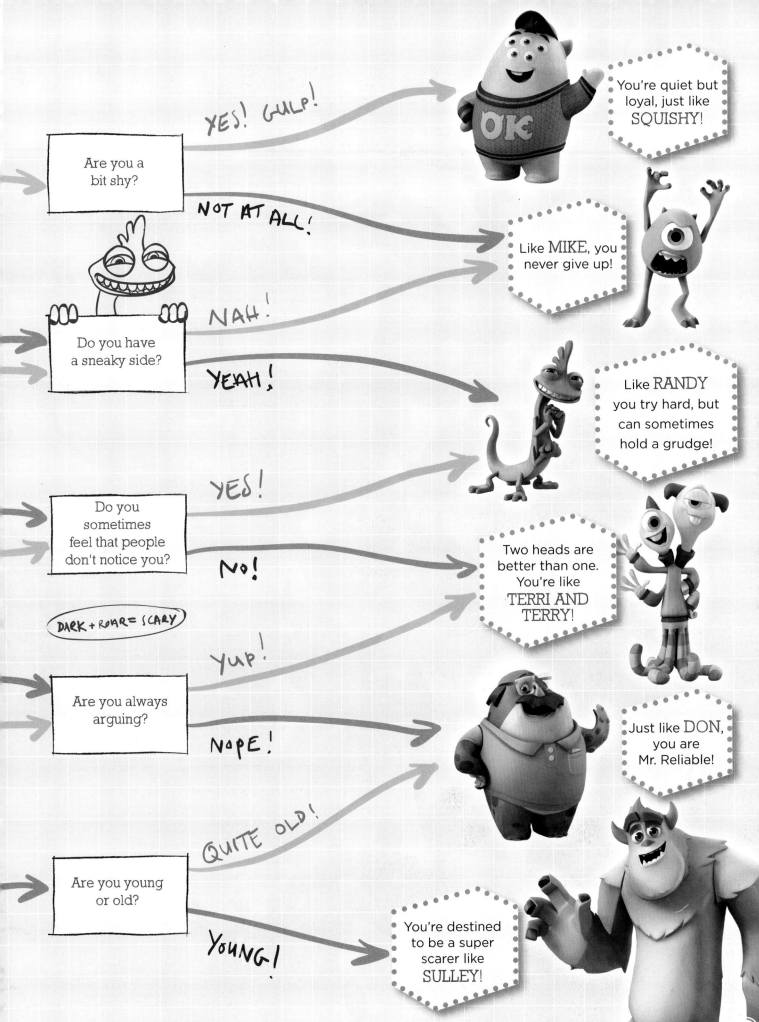

ALIEN AMBUSH

OOOOOOOH! Have you ever seen so many aliens? Oh, you have? Fair enough – but can you spot the eight that are slightly different from the rest?

22

MEMORY BOXES

How good is your memory?

Study these two pictures for a minute and then turn the page . . .

23

MEMORY BOX QUESTIONS

Answer these ten questions without peeking!

1. Davy Jones is carrying Mike.
TRUE / FALSE

2. Which Disney Princess costume is near Mr. Incredible?
A) Little Mermaid   **B)** Snow White   **C)** Cinderella

3. Which Disney Infinity Star DOESN'T appear in both pictures?
A) Jack Sparrow   **B)** Mr. Incredible   **C)** Buzz Lightyear

4. What Toy Box Set Piece does not appear in either picture?
A)   **B)**   **C)**

5. What colour is Jack's car?
A)   **B)**   **C)**

6. Who is riding Bullseye?
A)   **B)**   **C)**

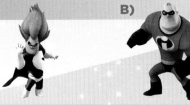 

7. What number is on the building in picture 2?
A) 8   **B)** 9   **C)** 10

8. In picture 1, what is growing on the rocks?
A) Blue flowers   **B)** Yellow flowers   **C)** Pink flowers

9. What is climbing the rock in picture 2?
A) A rope   **B)** A ladder   **C)** An elephant

10. Sulley is flying in Captain Hook's Ship.
TRUE / FALSE

How did you do?

0-2   Hmmm. You have a memory like a . . . what are those things called? We can't remember.

3-6   Not bad at all!

7+   You are a memory master!

PLAY SET

Think you know your Play Sets? Then you'll have no problem completing our crafty crossword . . .

CLUES

ACROSS

3. A lawman in need of help from the Lone Ranger (7)
5. The ideal number of eyes for an alien! (5)
8. A Wild West town that needs protection (5)
9. Arch-rivals of Sulley, Mike and co. (4,4)
11. A mean (but fun) trick to play in Radiator Springs (7,7)
13. A plant that can leave you snoozing (5,4)
14. Usually hangs around with Ragetti (6)
15. Anna's sister (4)
16. The youngest Incredible (4)

DOWN

1. The first person you save in the Pirates of the Caribbean Play Set (2,5)
2. The Lone Ranger's horse (6)
4. Sold by Fillmore (4)
6. Owns the Paint Shop in Radiator Springs (6)
7. 12 Down's new rank in Toy Story in Space (5,6)
10. An Agent found at NSA HQ (4,6)
12. He's green. He's a dinosaur. He's . . . who exactly? (3)
13. Mike's best friend (6)
14. Agent P's owner (7)

Crossword entries filled in:
- 5 Across: THREE
- 10 Down (partial): IN
- 12 Down: REX
- 13 Down: SULLEY
- 15 Across: ELSA
- 16 Across: DASH

Can you unscramble the letters in the yellow boxes to reveal an underwater terror?

25

DISNEY INFINITY'S
MOST WANTED

Boo, hiss! It's the biggest bad guys ever.
But who is the ultimate Disney Infinity enemy?
And which toy needs to be put back in his Toy Box?

SYNDROME

'SURRENDER! I HAVE ALREADY WON!'

Woah! Talk about scary! No, not Syndrome himself – look at that hair! Seriously, has he never heard of a comb? Unfortunately for the NSA, Syndrome has heard of world domination. He won't rest until he's brought the Incredibles to their knees.

- Fear Factor   4
- Fiendish Plots   6
- Evil Laugh   8
- Horrid Henchmen – Omnidroids   7
- Weapon – Zero Point Energy Gauntlets 4

DAVY JONES

'SUMMON THE KRAKEN!'

Shiver your timbers, it's the terror from the deep. Tentacle-faced Davy Jones is so bad he has his very own sea monster. No wonder the captain of the *Flying Dutchman*'s always in a bad mood. He can smell fish wherever he goes. Yuck!

- Fear Factor   8
- Fiendish Plots   6
- Evil Laugh   6
- Horrid Henchmen – Maccus   6
- Weapon – Cutlass   5

HERE BE MONSTERS!

How many monstrous Maleficents are on this page?

EMPEROR ZURG

'YOU WILL NOT SURVIVE!'

The arch-enemy of the Space Rangers doesn't want much in life – other than to wipe out Buzz Lightyear and the rest of the Toy Story gang, enslave all alien life forms and conquer most of the known universe. Actually, make that ALL of the known universe.

- Fear Factor   7
- Fiendish Plots   6
- Evil Laugh   7
- Horrid Henchmen – Zurgbots   7
- Weapon – Ion Blaster   8

BUTCH CAVENDISH

'LOOKS LIKE WE GOT OURSELVES A TOWN, BOYS!'

The people of Colby had a bright future until Butch Cavendish and his gang rode into town. Now, the band of outlaws control the railway that brings essential supplies. If only a masked hero and his Comanche partner were around to stop them!

- Fear Factor   5
- Fiendish Plots   5
- Evil Laugh   4
- Horrid Henchmen – The Cavendish Gang   7
- Weapon – Ball gun   6

TERRIBLE TRIO

It's not only big bads that heroes need to fight. There are tiny terrors too!

SNORING GLORIA

Able to send anyone to the land of nod with her doze-inducing Sleep Pods. Yawn! Anyone feeling tired?

BARON VON RUTHLESS

The beastly baron has invented a monstrous bomb that turns ordinary citizens into rampaging creatures. Rargh!

THE HOARDER

This crooked crook is forever setting complex traps for the poor people of Metroville.

CROSSOUT!

Scribble out any letter that appears more than once to reveal a devilish townsperson in the Toy Box . . .

B	T	G	V	C	O
F	H	I	W	X	K
L	Y	A	Z	I	W
T	L	Z	W	D	J
X	E	J	B	G	F
C	V	Y	S	O	K

Captain Jack Sparrow's Pirate DOs and DON'TS

Ahoy there, mate. So, you want to be a pirate? Then you need to learn from the best, and the best is Captain Jack Sparrow, savvy? Just follow his lead and you'll be buckling your swash in no time. But before you even strap on an eye-patch you need to follow these simple rules . . .

- **DO** choose yer mates wisely. You may need 'em to watch yer back.

- **DON'T** turn yer back on yer mates, just in case they double-cross you.

- **DO** say, 'May the beastie chase you down and use your gizzards for garters!'

- **DON'T** say, 'Down with pirates!' unless you want to be introduced to the Kraken.

- **DO** call your enemies 'scabby bilge-bags'. They deserve everything they get.

- **DON'T** call your parents 'scabby bilge-bags'. They won't like it one bit!

- **DO** swab the poop deck if asked.

- **DON'T** ask what the poop deck is. It's best not to know.

TRUE OR FALSE?

Have you been paying attention while exploring your Play Sets? Then try our True or False test. Be warned: Some are a bit tricky!

1 Students at Monsters University read *Fear-It Weekly* magazine.

TRUE | FALSE

2 There's a big W on the side of the Water Towers in Metroville.

TRUE | FALSE

3 Sarge is in Sarge's Hut in Radiator Springs.

TRUE | FALSE

4 The Cavendish Camp is set up right by the railroad.

TRUE | FALSE

5 The Toy Delivery Ship in Toy Story in Space is orange.

TRUE | FALSE

6 The second piece of the Kraken's Bane is found on Demon's Cape.

TRUE | FALSE

7 Fillmore's ultimate organic fuel is made from spicy red peppers.

TRUE | FALSE

8 Baron Von Ruthless's Monster Bombs are defused by dumping them into water.

TRUE | FALSE

9 The Thundering Stallion is the name of a saloon in Colby.

TRUE | FALSE

10 The Aliens' planet is found in the Gamma Sector of space.

TRUE | FALSE

DISNEY INFINITY A-Z

A **is for Archie the Scare Pig**
Who would have thought that the Fear Tech mascot would make such a great ride? But who would win a race between the horrid hog and Phillipe?

Who do you think would win? Write your winner here:
....

B **is for Boom!**
Adventure goes with a bang in Disney Infinity, especially if you're armed with a pesky Pirate Bomb or Colby TNT!

C **is for Critters**
Disney Infinity is crawling with critters but none are so rare as the Golden Skunk which can be found stinking up the place around Colby. Just hold your nose when you grab him! Eww!

D **is for Downloads**
Want to get your hands on some truly epic Toy Boxes? Then download worlds created by Disney's top designers by going to Toy Box Share on your games console. Maybe you could share your designs, too!

E **is for Enemy Creator**
Need to spice up your Toy Box? Then whack in an Enemy Creator to splurge out bad guys. All kinds of random nasties come out fighting at the touch of a button. Just listen for the air-raid siren when it turns on!

F **is for Frat Row**
When the Monsters are not studying (or goofing around on campus) they chill out in their Frat Houses. Just don't get locked out at night!

G is for Games Galore

Anyone for flamingo hockey? Or a quick game of Monsters vs. Pirates footie? You don't even have to use a ball. Just drop-kick a townsperson. GOAL!

H is for Hidden Mickeys

Hidden Mickeys are Mickey Mouse silhouettes that Disney designers hide in Disney films, books and theme parks. There are loads in Disney Infinity. How many have you spotted?

Here are three places to look for Hidden Mickeys:

* On Cinderella's Castle in the Toy Box
* Near Tia Dalma's House in the Pirates of the Caribbean Play Set
* On Luigi's Podium in the Cars Play Set

Can you find more?

I is for the Incredicar

Just how does Mr. Incredible reach crime scenes so fast? Why, in the super-cool Incredicar, of course. It goes 0-AWESOME in five seconds!

J is for Justice

Heroes can never rest in Disney Infinity. Whether it's the Lone Ranger cleaning up the streets of Colby, or Captain Jack trying to stop Davy Jones collecting souls, justice must always be served.

K is for Kraken's Bane

Handy if you're attacked by Davy Jones' pet sea monster, the Bane sends the Kraken back to the bottom of the ocean – but only if you can find the five pieces stashed on far-flung islands.

L is for Light Runner

This sci-fi speedster comes with its own techno soundtrack. Faster than the speed of, well, light . . .

M is for Metroville

The home of the Incredibles, Metroville is also the location of the National Supers Agency (NSA) HQ. This bustling city isn't always a safe place to live, thanks mainly to regular Omnidroid and super villain attacks.

N is for Nemo's Seascape
Ever fancied a PLAICE beneath the waves. Then turn your Play Set's sky into a SOLEful seascape. It's the next best FIN to actually being a fish!

What's your favourite sky texture for your Toy Box? Write it here:

O is for Omnidroids
Syndrome's robotic rotters come in many menacing models. Some fire homing missiles, while others pack laser-beam blasters. And watch out for mechanical monsters with scissor-claws for hands. Snap, snap!

P is for Power Discs
Able to give your character's abilities a timely boost, slipping a Power Disc onto your Disney Infinity Base can also unlock special mounts, melee weapons and new Play Set skylines and terrains.

How many Power Discs do you have? Write the number here:

Q is for Quests
Only one thing is impossible in Disney Infinity . . . getting bored! Have you completed all the quests and mini-missions in the Play Sets?

R is for Radiator Springs
It may look like a sleepy little backwater town, but the occupants of Radiator Springs are always racing around. Make sure you take a pit stop at Flo's V8 Cafe, get new tires at Luigi's Casa Della Tires and, when you need to rest your wheels, head for the Cozy Cone Motel.

S is for Songs
The Boom Box can blast out eighteen top Disney tunes, from the *Mickey Mouse Club March* to tracks from *The Nightmare Before Christmas* and *Tron* soundtracks. Which one's your favourite? Write it down here:

T is for Teleporter
Handy for getting around your Toy Box in a flash, teleporters are Creativi-Toys that zap you from one place to another.

U is for Unlockables
Make sure you unlock each Play Set's character chests for a host of toys and themed Toy Box Worlds. How many have you unlocked so far?

V is for Vault
If you need more toys in your Toy Box, then head to the Disney Infinity Toy Vault. As you play the game you earn 'Spins' that allow you to randomly select Toys when you next unlock the Vault. What will you get next time?

W is for Wand
Always keep your wand handy in the Toy Box. The Magic Wand helps you build amazing tracks and buildings, while the purpose of the Invisibility Wand is clear to see. Or rather, it isn't.

X is for X-Games
Build your own X-Games stunt park in your Toy Box. Show off some serious skills on the rad ramps, platforms and pipes.

Z is for Zurgbots
Move over Omnidroids. Zurgbots are just as sinister as Syndrome's sneaky creations. Some have massive spiked balls for hands. Some shoot missiles or energy balls. Some smother you in goo. ALL should be avoided!

Y is for Yo Ho Ho!
The call of every good pirate (and quite a few bad ones as well!)

MONSTER

MONSTERS LOVE PLAYING PRANKS ON EACH OTHER — ALMOST US MUCH AS WE LIKE SCARING HUMANS. IF YOU'RE GOING TO MAKE IT AT MONSTERS UNIVERSITY, YOU NEED TO MASTER THESE BASIC PRACTICAL JOKES. LET'S START AT THE BEGINNING . . .

How mad do you think each prank will make those Fear Tech jocks? Rate each by shading the Grrr! bar.

One = not that bothered.
Four = hopping mad!

GRRR! | 1 | 2 | 3 | 4 |

SNEAK AND SCREAM

Shhh! Sneak up behind a FT monster and let rip with a deafening roar. A loudhailer can help if your roar is a bit on the weedy side!

SNEAK AND SCREAM

GRRR! | 1 | 2 | 3 | 4 |

TOILET ROLLED

GRRR! | 1 | 2 | 3 | 4 |

TOILET ROLLED

Cover Fear Tech statues in toilet paper. You might as well do the trees at the same time. Heh!

PRANKS

A BANNER DAY

Drape 'MU Rocks!' banners all over the Fear Tech Dorms. It's true, you know. We majorly rock!

A BANNER DAY   1 2 3 4
GRRR!

ADD A LITTLE COLOUR   1 2 3 4
GRRR!

ADD A LITTLE COLOUR

Redecorate Fear Tech recruitment posters with paintball pellets. Splat, splat, splat!

LEND A HAND

Install Give 'Em a Hand Launcher all over campus. When a FT student comes near – SLAP! They won't know what hit them!

LEND A HAND   1 2 3 4
GRRR!

WATCH OUT!

Keep your eyes peeled* for Fear Tech jokers. Here are just some of the pranks they've pulled on us!

*the more eyes you have the better, of course.

SEE-THROUGH SNEAKS

What? Some of them can turn invisible? Good job we've got Randy. Has anyone seen him?

TOILET ROLL MUMMIES

Tying one of our students to the flagpole using toilet paper? He was left a bit flushed!

TICK TOCK

Poor old Terri and Terry were left in knots at the top of the Clock Tower. Time for revenge, I think!

OTHER SURPRISES INCLUDE:

Fly Swatter Launcher – You'll be buzzing after this one goes off.
Incoming Call Ender – A phone booth that packs a punch!
Leafing So Soon? – This pile of leaves will help you turn over a new FT loser!
School Colors Ender – Give FT students a MU makeover.

YUCK!

Unscramble the word to reveal a gooey trick!

DULSEG OBLALNO!

43

FRANCESCO'S TIME TRIAL

Race Francesco Bertoulli through these puzzles!

1 Which three jigsaw pieces fit the picture puzzle?

A)

B)

C)

D)

E)

F)

G)

H)

I)

The correct pieces are:

☐ ☐ ☐

Francesco's time = 3 mins

Your time = ☐ mins

2 Which name below doesn't fit into the grid?

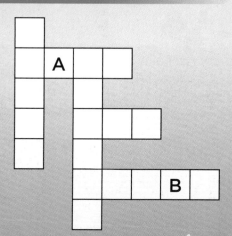

A

B

☐ Art   ☐ Hamm
☐ Chick   ☐ Mirage
☐ Gibbs   ☐ Red

Francesco's time = 5 mins

Your time = ☐ mins

3 STAR SPLICE
Which three Disney Infinity Stars have been mashed together?

They are:

A)

B)

C)

Francesco's time = 3 mins

Your time = ☐ mins

5 SHADOW SAILOR
Davy Jones has always been a shady character, but which of these shadows perfectly matches the tentacled terror?

A)

B)

C)

D)

E)

F)

The correct shadow is: ☐

Francesco's time = 5 mins

Your time = ☐ mins

4 Unscramble this word to reveal the name of a miserly Toy Box Set Piece.

RSOCSGO'E
NMYEO NBI

Francesco's time = 4 mins

Your time = ☐ mins

HOW DID YOU DO?
Francesco roared through the puzzles in twenty minutes. How did you do?

I did it in . . . ☐ minutes.

45

RACETRACK RIOT

It's race day in the Toy Box and everybody wants to take part! Ten sparks are hidden in this jam-packed scene. Can you find them all, as well as the toys listed below?

Lightning McQueen

Francesco

Holley

Mater

Sparks

FINISH

WAND-NAPPED!

Someone has taken Elsa's Disney Infinity Wand. Solve the clues to discover which culprit is responsible!

Eliminate the suspects as you work through the clues!

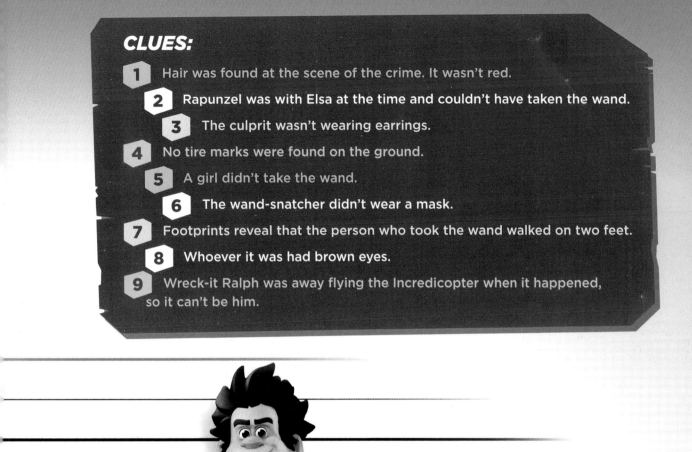

CLUES:

1 Hair was found at the scene of the crime. It wasn't red.

2 Rapunzel was with Elsa at the time and couldn't have taken the wand.

3 The culprit wasn't wearing earrings.

4 No tire marks were found on the ground.

5 A girl didn't take the wand.

6 The wand-snatcher didn't wear a mask.

7 Footprints reveal that the person who took the wand walked on two feet.

8 Whoever it was had brown eyes.

9 Wreck-it Ralph was away flying the Incredicopter when it happened, so it can't be him.

49

WANT SOME NIFTY NEW ABILITIES IN YOUR PLAY SETS AND TOY BOX WORLDS? THEN TRY OUT THESE CRAZY POWER DISC COMBINATIONS!

POWER DISC

BETTER SPARK SHIELD

Add Star Command Shield to Pieces of Eight and 3% of your damage will be converted into Sparks.

NIFTY NICELANDERS

Want to up your experience rate by 5%? Then you need Ralph's Power of Destruction plus Fix-It Felix's Repair Power.

HEALTH BOOST

Pile up Chernabog's Power on top of Sorcerer's Apprentice Mickey's Hat for a 5% health boost. Magic!

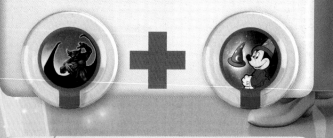

SUPER SPARK SHIELD

If you want 4% more sparks when you defeat enemies then grab Violet's Force Field and Pieces of Eight.

GIRL POWER

Pop Violet's Force Field and Rapunzel's Healing Power together and you'll cause 5% more damage. Go, girls!

SCIENCE FIX

When Fix-It Felix's Repair Power and Dr Doofenshmirtz's Damage-Inator get together you get 5% better health regeneration. Nice!

COOL COMBOS!

INCREDIBLE PICKUP

Wish you could boost your pickup range by a whopping 50%? Then what are you waiting for? Combine Violet's Force Field with Bolt's Super Strength!

LIGHTNING SHIELD

Bad guys beware! Bounce 5% of damage back onto your attackers with Bolt's Super Strength and Electro-Charge. Pow!

Your Dream Power Disc

Imagine you could create your own Power Disc. What would it be?

What kind of Power Disc is it?
- [ ] Ability
- [ ] Toy
- [ ] Customization

Which Disney film or character would you base it on?

What would it do?

What would you call it?

TYPES OF DISCS

Circular Power Discs

These round discs give your Disney Infinity figures special powers in your Play Sets and the Toy Box.

Toy Power Discs

These hexagonal discs add new gadgets, vehicles and weapons to your Toy Box.

Customization Power Discs

Give your Toy Box a mega-makeover with new landscapes and skylines.

The orange Power Discs are the rarest of all! Have you collected any?

TOY BOX SUPER SHARES

Disney Infinity fans all around the world are creating amazing Toy Boxes packed with games and challenges. Here's our pick of the best creations found in Toy Box Share. Have you played them yet?

TICK THE ONE THAT LOOKS THE MOST EXCITING!

■ The BIG Room
by Enrem

When Andy's away, the toys will play! Disney Infinity Community member Enrem built this brilliant Toy Box based on Andy's Room from *Toy Story*. Head up to the bed to find some cars ready to race on a twisty track or ride the rail around the walls. There's even table football, if you can get past the baddies on the way, that is.

■ Light Cycle Grid
by Warlord Raven

Created by Warlord Raven, this high-tech racer drops you into the virtual world of Tron. Race Light Cycles on the multilevel track or run around the arena to collect some welcome sparks. And if you don't want to travel by teleporter, there's a Recognizer hidden somewhere on the grid. Can you find it?

Mad Valentines
by Cthulius

Off with her head! The Queen of Hearts has stolen all the candies from the Mad Hatter's Valentine Party. What a rotter! Community member Cthulius's totally bonkers Toy Box is a real labour of love. Find the candies hidden away in the middle of maddening mazes, puzzling pits or the end of impossible obstacle courses. Oh, and watch out for that Cheshire Cat!

Ursula's Revenge
by Crazybynick

3:37

Ursula the Sea Witch has returned from the depths to kidnap an entire family of mermaids. Crazybynick's underwater Toy Box challenges you to rescue them all before the clock runs out. Slide from world to world to free the Little Mermaids from danger.

Paintball Mania
by Spiderfan1978

It's the ultimate paintball fight! Dive into the arena and find your paintball gun before the other team starts trying to redecorate you! The first team to reach twenty-one hits will win – and there's even a handy cannon, in case you fancy some heavier firepower. Get splatting!

JACK SKELLINGTON'S HORRIBLE HOWLERS

The Pumpkin King loves a good bone-tickler.
How funny are these gruesome gags?
Rate each one – if you dare!

HOW DO SKELETONS TALK TO THEIR FRIENDS?

ON THE TELE-BONE!

NOT FUNNY | | | | | | | DEAD FUNNY

WHAT'S A VAMPIRE'S FAVOURITE FRUIT?

NECK-TARINES!

NOT FUNNY | | | | | | | DEAD FUNNY

WHAT KIND OF MONSTER IS ALWAYS PLAYING TRICKS?

PRANK-ENSTEIN!

NOT FUNNY | | | | | | | DEAD FUNNY

HOW DO YOU TELL THE TIME AT HALLOWEEN?

WITH A WITCH WATCH!

NOT FUNNY | | | | | | | DEAD FUNNY

HOW DO MONSTERS LIKE TO COOK PEOPLE?

TERROR-FRIED!

NOT FUNNY | | | | | | | DEAD FUNNY

WHAT IS AN OGRE'S FAVOURITE SCHOOL GAME?

SWALLOW THE LEADER!

NOT FUNNY | | | | | | | DEAD FUNNY

WHAT DID THE POLICEMAN SAY WHEN HE MET THE MONSTER WITH TWO HEADS?

'HELLO, HELLO!'

NOT FUNNY | | | | | | | DEAD FUNNY

WHAT GAME SHOULD YOU NEVER PLAY WITH GIANTS?

SQUASH!

NOT FUNNY | | | | | | | DEAD FUNNY

DID YOU HEAR ABOUT THE TOY PIG THAT WAS BITTEN BY DRACULA?

IT BECAME A HAMM-PIRE!

NOT FUNNY | | | | | | | DEAD FUNNY

WHY ARE GHOSTS POLITE?

THEY DON'T SPOOK UNTIL THEY'RE SPOKEN TO!

NOT FUNNY | | | | | | | DEAD FUNNY

THE DIFFERENCE

Agent P and Phineas are having trouble with Zurgbots. Can you find ten differences between the two pictures?

WHAT HAPPENS

1. *Oh no! Agent P and Mike are being terrorised by Zurgbots.*

One: The heroes get knocked all the way to the next Toy Box. Ouch!

Two: Rapunzel blasts the bots using her Cinderella Carriage rocket. Blam!

Three: Agent P pulls out a Goo Shrinker and shrinks the menace!

Four: Mrs. Incredible swoops down on Condor Man's wings and saves them. Hurray!

Five: The Zurgbots get frozen by Elsa. Brrrrrr.

Six: Mike whacks the bots with his hidden Identity Disc.

2. *Whoops! Barbossa's Hover Board runs out of juice in mid-air . . .*

One: He tumbles into Scrooge McDuck's Money Bin and gets stuck inside! Help, me hearties!

Two: He lands on a rail and zips down to safety.

Three: No problem! He switches to Buzz Lightyear's Rocket Pack.

Four: He crashes down on an Agrabah Guard. Soft Landing!

Five: Dash saves him in the Attack Copter.

Six: Davy Jones catches him with his tentacles. Who would have guessed, me hearties?

NEXT?

3. *Sorcerer's Apprentice Mickey gets a surprise gift. What's in it?*

One: A Captain Hook Costume. Shucks! That'll never fit.

Two: A new Elasti-Hand. Oh boy!

Three: A teleporter that zaps him into Syndrome's clutches. Aaargh!

Four: Splat! A slime pie in the face! Those pesky MU guys!

Five: The Golden Skunk. Ugh!

Six: Ticking dynamite from the Cavendish gang. Run!

4. *Maximus the Horse steps on a Power Switch by accident! What's it connected to?*

One: An Enemy Generator. Get ready to rumble!

Two: A Falling Object Generator. Bowling Balls start raining down. Look out below!

Three: A Boom Box. Oh no! It's playing Frankenweenie. Scary.

Four: A Party Cannon. Ooooh, fireworks!

Five: Invulnerable Beacon. Just in time! Maccus is charging towards us.

Six: A Friend Generator. Phew! It's only Bullseye.

5. *Holley is racing Violet in the Pizza Planet Delivery Truck and they're neck and neck!*

One: Violet races over some exploding mines. Boom!

Two: Holley gets knocked off the track by a swinging pendulum. Thwack!

Three: A masher comes crashing in on either side of Violet!

Four: Holley drives over a Grow Panel and gets supersized.

Five: Violet wins. Incredible!

Six: Holley races to victory. Yay!

ARE YOU A DISNEY INFINITY BRIGHT SPARK?

It's time to test your Disney Infinity knowledge. How well do you know this incredible game?

1 What is the name of the cards that MU monsters collect?
A) Fear-It Cards
B) Scare Cards
C) Monster Cards

2 What is Vanellope also known as?
A) The Glitch
B) The Grouch
C) The Glutton

3 What prize does Captain Jack get after defeating Davy Jones?
A) The Kraken Helmet
B) The Kraken Horn
C) The Kraken Hammer

4 What is the name of the engine that pulls the Colby Express Train?
A) The Constitution Engine
B) The Coronation Engine
C) The Celebration Engine

5 Who does Finn McMissile work for?
A) C.R.O.N.I.C.
B) C.H.R.O.M.E.
C) C.R.O.N.E.

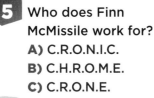

6 What's on the side of the batteries in Toy Story in Space?
A) A bolt
B) A star
C) A moon

7 Name this
character:
A) Moon
B) Mirage
C) Midnight

8 What number is
on the side of
Chick Hick?
A) 66
B) 76
C) 86

9 How many
eyes does
Squishy have?
A) Four
B) Five
C) Six

10 What is the name of the
Native American tribe
that lives near Colby?
A) The Comanche
B) The Cherokee
C) The Chickasaw

12 Which colour bead
DOESN'T Captain Jack
Sparrow wear in his hair?

A)

B)

C)

11 How does Edna
come to Metroville?
A) By train
B) By car
C) By helicopter

13 What can Agent P
throw to take
out enemies?
A) His hat
B) His tail
C) Phineas

14 What does Flo run in
Radiator Springs?
A) The Motel
B) The Paint Shop
C) The Café

15 How many animals
escape from
Metroville Zoo?
A) Four
B) Six
C) Eight

SPACE SCRAMBLE

Buzz Lightyear has hidden a special message in this colourful grid.
Start with the letter in the middle of the grid and use the coloured key
to work out which direction you should read to complete the message.

KEY

Write the message here:

ANSWERS

Page 10 – Word Up!

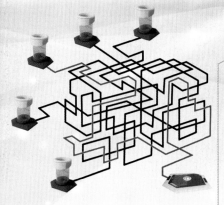

The hidden villains are Baron Von Ruthless, Snoring Gloria and the Hoarder.

Page 17 – Get the Party Started

Page 17 – What Comes Next?
1. Timer   2. Target

Page 22 – Alien Ambush

Pages 23–4 – Memory Boxes
1. FALSE   5. C   9. A
2. B   6. B   10. TRUE
3. C   7. A
4. B   8. C

Page 25 – Play Set Puzzler

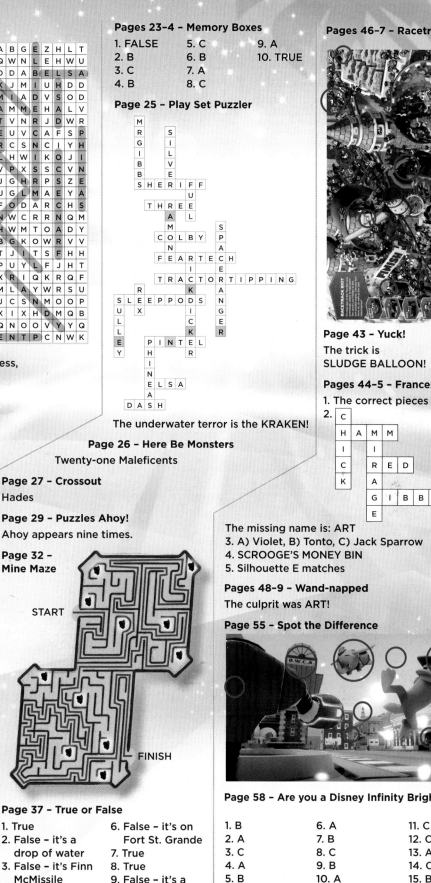

The underwater terror is the KRAKEN!

Page 26 – Here Be Monsters
Twenty-one Maleficents

Page 27 – Crossout
Hades

Page 29 – Puzzles Ahoy!
Ahoy appears nine times.

Page 32 – Mine Maze

START

FINISH

Page 37 – True or False
1. True
2. False – it's a drop of water
3. False – it's Finn McMissile
4. True
5. True
6. False – it's on Fort St. Grande
7. True
8. True
9. False – it's a spirit horse
10. True

Pages 46–7 – Racetrack Riot

RACETRACK RIOT

Page 43 – Yuck!
The trick is SLUDGE BALLOON!

Pages 44–5 – Francesco's Time Trial
1. The correct pieces are: C, E and G
2.

The missing name is: ART
3. A) Violet, B) Tonto, C) Jack Sparrow
4. SCROOGE'S MONEY BIN
5. Silhouette E matches

Pages 48–9 – Wand-napped
The culprit was ART!

Page 55 – Spot the Difference

Page 58 – Are you a Disney Infinity Bright Spark?
1. B   6. A   11. C
2. A   7. B   12. C
3. C   8. C   13. A
4. A   9. B   14. C
5. B   10. A   15. B

Page 60 – Space Scramble
The message is:
THE ALIENS ARE TRAPPED IN THE HOSPITAL